BEAU PEEP BOOK 11

From The

DAILY STAR

© 1990
Express Newspapers plc,
245 Blackfriars Road,
London, SE1 9UX.
Printed by Grosvenor Press
(Portsmouth) Ltd.,
Reproduction by
Graphic Origination, London
Co-ordinated by
Roeder Print Services Ltd.,
London.
Researched by
Terry Greenwood

ISBN 0-85079-208-8

£2·5ſ

BEAU PEEP

EGON

THE NOMAD

MAD PIERRE

SERGEANT BIDET

COLONEL ESCARGOT

THE VULTURE

A picture of the writer, Roger Kettle (left) and artist, Andrew Christine, shortly after they tossed to decide who got to wear the jacket.

THE ADVENTURES OF LEGIONNAIRE
BEAU PEEP

FROM THE **Star** DAILY

I'M OFF TO SEE ASTRO THE SOOTHSAYER.

2703

HE'S WORKING ON MY CHARTS FOR THE FUTURE.

IT AMAZES ME HOW HE SEEMS TO KNOW EVERYTHING.

IS THAT YOU, MUM?

ASTRO THE SOOTHSAYER

YOU WANT TO KNOW HOW RICH AND FAMOUS YOU'LL BE?

YES!

2704

DO YOU WISH THE STANDARD OR DE LUXE VERSION?

WHAT'S THE DIFFERENCE?

IN THE 'DE-LUXE' VERSION, I TRY NOT TO LAUGH.

SERGEANTS' EXAM
YOU WISH YOUR MEN TO FIX BAYONETS.

LIST THE THREE COMMANDS COVERING THE PROCEDURE.

Stab! Stab! Stab!

2724

SERGEANTS' EXAM:—
WHAT IS A BLOCKADE?

2725

It's what you'll get in the mouth for asking stupid questions.

HOW DID YOU DO IN THE EXAM?

I FAILED.

THEY SAID I WAS OVER-ENTHUSIASTIC.

APPARENTLY WE'RE NOT ALLOWED TO THROTTLE RECRUITS FOR WHISTLING.

2726

Panel 1: WHAT DID YOU USED TO DO AT CHRISTMAS?

Panel 2: MY MUM AND DAD WERE KEEN ON THAT THING WITH LITTLE HOUSES AND HOTELS.

Panel 3: MONOPOLY? / NO, BREAKING AND ENTERING.

Panel 4: ...IT WAS CHRISTMAS EVE AND I'D ALWAYS WANTED A PUPPY...

Panel 5: ...AND, IN DAD'S WARDROBE, I FOUND A BOX WITH LITTLE HOLES IN THE TOP.

Panel 6: I WAS SO HAPPY I OPENED IT. / AND?

Panel 7: HIS FISHING MAGGOTS GOT AWAY.

Panel 8: I'D GIVEN UP HOPE OF GETTING A PUPPY...

Panel 9: ...THEN ONE CHRISTMAS I AWOKE TO THE SOUND OF YAPPING AND BARKING.

Panel 10: AW, THAT'S NICE...

Panel 11: THOSE POLICE DOGS MAKE A HELL OF A NOISE!

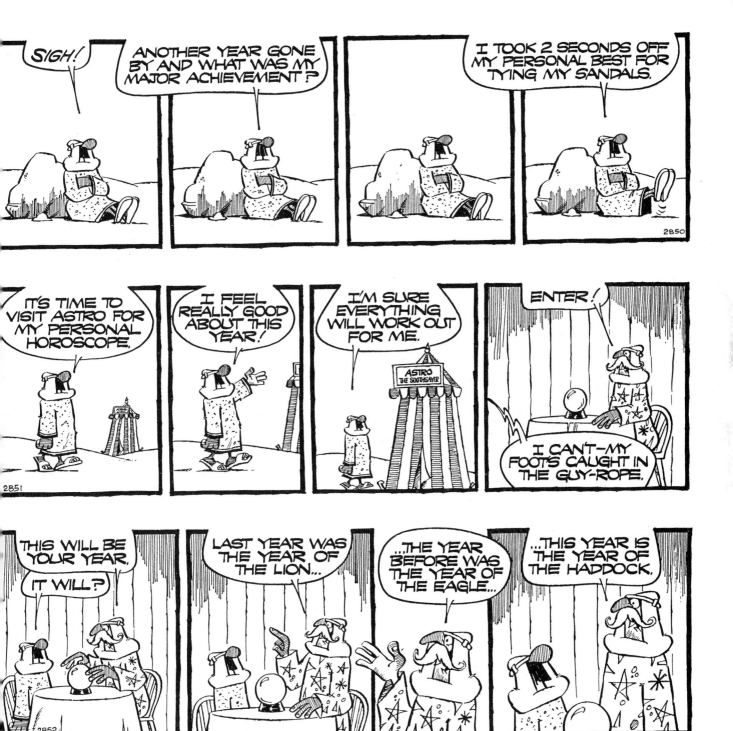

THERE'S THAT VULTURE AGAIN.

IT GIVES ME THE SHIVERS THE WAY IT JUST SITS THERE.

I WONDER WHAT IT THINKS ABOUT?

IN THE HOKEY-COKEY, IS IT THE LEFT OR RIGHT LEG THAT GOES IN FIRST?

2868

I'M STARVING — I HAVEN'T SEEN A DEAD GOAT IN AGES.

THERE'S A HERD OF THEM OVER THERE, ALL FROLICKING AROUND.

IF THERE'S ONE THING THAT GETS UP MY NOSE IT'S HEALTHY GOATS!

2869

JUST LOOK AT THAT — ANOTHER HERD OF GOATS PRANCING ABOUT...

...EVERY ONE OF THEM FIT AND HEALTHY-LOOKING, AND SKIPPING AND DANCING!

THERE'S ONLY ONE THING WORSE THAN A HEALTHY GOAT AND THAT'S A SMUG GOAT!

2870

THIS LIFESTYLE OF MINE IS GETTING TO ME.

I SPEND ALL MY TIME WAITING AROUND FOR GOATS TO DIE.

AS A CAREER THAT RANKS RIGHT ALONGSIDE ACCOUNTANCY.

2871

MAYBE I'M BEING TOO NARROW IN MY OUTLOOK.

WHO SAYS VULTURES HAVE TO LEAD BORING LIVES AS SCAVENGERS?

WHAT'S TO STOP ME HUNTING AND KILLING MY OWN PREY?

DAMN. NO RIFLE.

2872

THAT VULTURE'S STILL SITTING THERE.

ALL THAT WAITING— THEY MUST BE EXTREMELY PATIENT CREATURES.

DAMN AND BLAST IT! THAT'S IT—I'M OFF!

2873

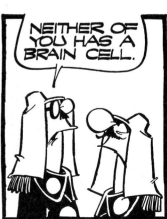

MEN CAN LOOK VERY DASHING WITH A MOUSTACHE.

2883

MY DORIS ALWAYS USED TO LIKE THEM.

THAT'S PROBABLY WHY SHE GREW HER OWN.

I THINK I LOOK HANDSOME WITH MY MOUSTACHE...

...YOU KNOW, LIKE THAT ACTOR WITH THE MOUSTACHE AND THE BIG EARS.

LASSIE?

2884

I SHAVED OFF MY MOUSTACHE.

WHY?

2885

TO STOP PEOPLE SAYING I LOOK STUPID.

YOU HAD A SHAVE, DENNIS, NOT PLASTIC SURGERY.

IT'S TIME I STARTED MY WRITING CAREER AGAIN.

I THINK I'LL DO A REAL TEAR-JERKER THIS TIME.

"Here," He said, "That's my Dog you've just run over."

2916

I'VE CRACKED THE SECRET OF SUCCESSFUL WRITING!

WHAT YOU DO IS PINCH SOMEONE ELSE'S WORK AND ADAPT IT SLIGHTLY.

Romeo and Daphne."

2917

I'M GOING TO MAKE MY NEW BOOK A REAL "WEEPIE."

SAD STORIES ARE ALWAYS BEST-SELLERS.

MAYBE I SHOULD JUST PUBLISH MY BANK STATEMENTS.

2918

Panel 1: SNIFF! THIS IS THE SADDEST STORY I'VE EVER WRITTEN!

Panel 2: "AFTER HIS PUPPY DIED, THE LITTLE ORPHAN WAS LOST AND HUNGRY..."

Panel 3: "...HIS MUMMY WAS ILL AND SOMEONE STOOD ON HIS GLASSES."

Panel 4: THAT'S MAYBE A BIT LONG FOR A TITLE.

2919

Panel 5: BOO-HOO-HOO! — WHAT'S THE MATTER?

Panel 6: I'VE JUST WRITTEN THE SADDEST STORY EVER...

Panel 7: ...BUT EVEN THROUGH THE TEARS, I'VE INJECTED A LITTLE HUMOUR.

Panel 8: WHAT'S IT CALLED? — "ORPHANS A GO-GO."

2920

Panel 9: I'VE GOT A LETTER FROM YOUR PUBLISHER.

Panel 10: I CAN'T LOOK! YOU OPEN IT FOR ME!

Panel 11: ARE YOU SITTING COMFORTABLY? — YES! YES!

Panel 12: YOU WON'T BE IF YOU DO WHAT HE SUGGESTS WITH YOUR BOOK.

2921

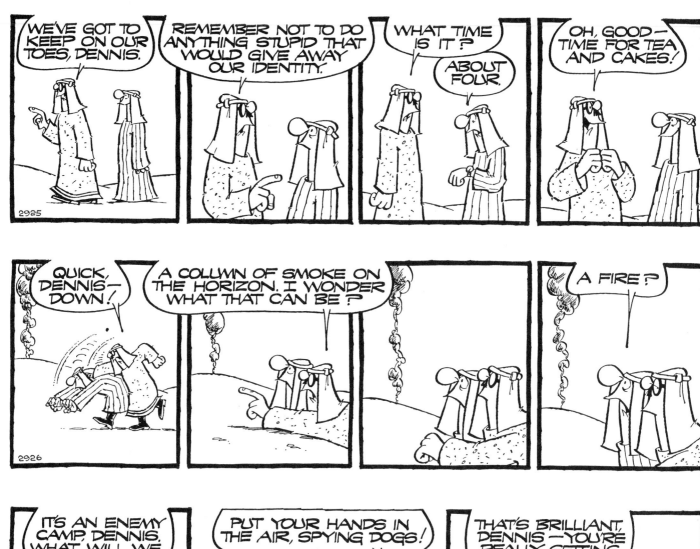

2928

2929

930

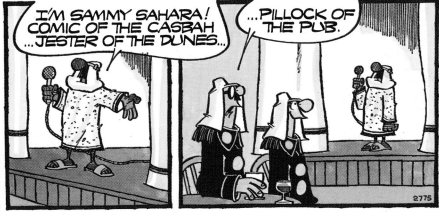

MY THROW NOW...
YIPPEE! SEVEN!

TOSS!

ONE... ER...
TWO... ER...

DENNIS?

COULD YOU EXPLAIN HOW YOU GET SEVEN FROM ONE DICE?

DUNNO—JUST LUCKY, I GUESS...
ER... TEN... ER... FOUR...

AN EIGHT! BRILLIANT!

I'LL JUST SHOOT UP THIS SNAKE!

WHEEE!

WHEN BRAINS WERE BEING GIVEN OUT, YOU MUST HAVE BEEN IN THE HADDOCK QUEUE.

DENNIS, SNAKES AND LADDERS IS A SIMPLE GAME!

I KNOW!

IT'S UP THE LADDERS AND—

I'M NOT STUPID!

WELL, PLAY IT PROPERLY!

I AM!

WHOSE DEAL IS IT?

Panel 1: OH, LOOK—IT'S THE COLONEL'S DAUGHTER.

Panel 2: THREE... FOUR... FIVE... SIX...

Panel 3: COOEE! LOOK AT MY MUSCLES!

Panel 4: ...SEVEN SECONDS TO MAKE A TOTAL IDIOT OF HIMSELF.

2804

Panel 5: DENNIS, WHY ARE YOU WEARING SUNGLASSES?

2805

Panel 6: I'M TRYING TO IMPRESS THE COLONEL'S DAUGHTER.

Panel 7: STUPIDITY IMPRESSES HER?

Panel 8: HERE COMES THE COLONEL'S DAUGHTER.

Panel 9: BE POLITE AND FORMAL—CALL HER "MA'AM."

Panel 10: GIVE US A BIG, JUICY KISS, MA'AM!

2806

IT'S SHEER HELL BEING A POET.

YOU CAN SPEND HOURS SEARCHING FOR JUST ONE PRECISE WORD.

THERE MUST BE SOMETHING RHYMES WITH "BURP"!

2825

WHAT ARE YOU DOING?

2826

I'M WRITING AN EPIC LOVE POEM.

IT'S ABOUT MY PURE AND DEVOTED LOVE FOR A SHY YOUNG MAIDEN.

HOW MANY "Z's ARE THERE IN "BAZOOKAS"?

THIS POEM OF YOURS IS AWFUL!

YOU'VE OBVIOUSLY GOT NO SOUL, NO EMOTION, NO ROMANCE!

"YOU'VE GOT NOSTRILS LIKE A PIG" IS THE BEST THING I'VE WRITTEN!

2827